My little **purple** book of

stories

and

pictures

45 Old Testament stories
and activities
for young children

Material also available as A4 photocopiable group resource
Stories and Pictures Old Testament, first published 2011

Scripture Union
207–209 Queensway, Bletchley, Milton Keynes, MK2 2EB
Email: info@scriptureunion.org.uk
Website: www.scriptureunion.org.uk

Scripture Union Australia
Locked Bag 2, Central Coast Business Centre, NSW 2252
Website: www.scriptureunion.org.au

Scripture Union USA
PO Box 215, Valley Forge, PA 19481 USA
Website: www.scriptureunion.org

Scripture quotations are from the Contemporary English
Version published by HarperCollinsPublishers © 1991, 1992,
1995 American Bible Society.

Children's retellings of Bible stories previously published in
Bubbles for Children or *The Big Bible Storybook*, © Scripture
Union 2006.

British Library Cataloguing-in-Publication Data
A catalogue record of this book is available from the
British Library.

Printed and bound in Singapore by Tien Wah Press

Cover and internal design: kwgraphicdesign
Cover photography: Steve Shipman
Illustrations: Sonia Canals
Tiddlywinks series editor: Maggie Barfield
Writer: Maggie Barfield
Freelance editor and project manager: Louise Titley

Scripture Union is an international charity working with
churches in more than 130 countries, providing resources to
bring the good news of Jesus Christ to children, young people
and families and to encourage them to develop spiritually
through the Bible and prayer.

As well as our network of volunteers, staff and associates
who run holidays, church-based events and school Christian
groups, we produce a wide range of publications and support
those who use our resources through training programmes.

Contents

How to use this book

All the activities in this book can be used to introduce your child to a Bible story, or to remind them of a Bible story that you have just shared together and to get them involved in more of the detail. Each picture activity is designed to stimulate further thought on, and discussion of, the Bible story at the level of under-5s, as well as to provide them with plenty of fun!

Before you start, read through the notes to check you have all the art materials you need. Most of the activities need only crayons, paints, glue and collage materials, but some of them do use some less everyday art materials to get particular effects.

Have fun! Your relationship with your child can tell them as much about God's love for them as the retelling of a Bible story.

Why not read the story from the Bible yourself before you start, to remind yourself of the details?

A taster verse or two of the actual Bible text is also given. You could use this to help your child relate the Bible stories to a complete Bible. Try looking up the verse in your Bible and showing your child the same words on the Bible page. (All actual Bible text used here comes from the CEV translation.)

Tell the story. The retelling of each Bible story has been written in a way that is accessible to under-5s.

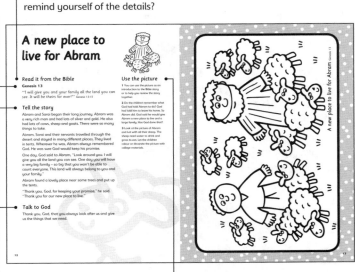

A new place to live for Abram

Read it from the Bible

Genesis 13

"I will give you and your family all the land you can see. It will be theirs for ever!" Genesis 13:15

Tell the story

Abram and Sarai began their long journey. Abram was a very rich man and had lots of silver and gold. He also had lots of cows, sheep and goats. There were so many things to take.

Abram, Sarai and their servants travelled through the desert and stayed in many different places. They lived in tents. Wherever he was, Abram always remembered God. He was sure God would keep his promise.

One day, God said to Abram, "Look around you. I will give you all the land you can see. One day you will have a very big family – so big that you won't be able to count everyone. This land will always belong to you and your family."

Abram found a lovely place near some trees and put up the tents.

"Thank you, God, for keeping your promise," he said. "Thank you for our new place to live."

Talk to God

Thank you, God, that you always look after us and give us the things that we need.

Use the picture

1 You can use the picture as an introduction to the Bible story or to help you review the story together.

2 Do the children remember what God had told Abram to do? God had told him to leave his home. So Abram did. God said he would give Abram a new place to live and a large family. Has God done that?

3 Look at the picture of Abram and Lot with all their sheep. The sheep need water to drink and grass to eat. Let the children colour or decorate the picture with collage materials.

Talk to God. Each activity is rounded off with the words of a prayer or an idea for a prayer topic.

Use the picture! Each activity gives you ideas on how to get the most from each Bible picture, stimulating further exploration of the story.

Light to live by

Read it from the Bible

Psalm 119:9–16,105

'Your word is a lamp
that gives light wherever I walk.' *Psalm 119:105*

Tell the story

When God made the world, the very first thing he made was light. Bright, bright, shining light! Gleaming, glinting, beautiful light.

God's world was a wonderful place for people to live. There was sunlight in the daytime and moonlight at night.

At first, people were happy living in God's world. But then they began fighting, telling lies, being unkind and not caring for the earth.

God was sad. It was as though his beautiful world was darker.

"I want people to live my way," God said. "I will speak to them."

God told his people how to be happy and enjoy his world. Some people would not listen, but others decided, "Let's write down what God says."

Now we can hear what God is saying in the Bible!

It is like a shining light, helping us see how to live God's way.

Talk to God

Thank you, God, that you can speak to us through stories in the Bible.

Use the picture

1 You can use the picture as an introduction to the Bible story or to help you review the story together.

2 Ask the children to help you make a display of Bibles and children's Bible storybooks if you have them. What is the same about all these books? They tell us about God and they are all ways of helping us to hear what God is saying to us.

3 Look at the Bible-story picture and complete the scene of the children looking at a book together. What are the children in the picture doing?

4 Let your children copy what those in the picture are doing and examine the books. If you have time, they could choose a story to have read aloud.

5 Be enthusiastic about the Bible yourself and tell the children your favourite Bible story.

6 Help them to think about a story they like from the Bible. Can they draw a picture from their favourite Bible story on a blank sheet of paper?

God makes land, sea and plants

Read it from the Bible

Genesis 1:9–13

'God named the dry ground "Land", and he named the water "Sea". God looked at what he had done and saw that it was good.' *Genesis 1:10*

Tell the story

God's new world was covered with water. God said, "I want to make the sea and the land." All at once, the water rushed together.

It made seas and rivers, lakes and ponds, oceans and puddles.

And that left the dry earth. God made it into rocky mountains, gentle hills, dry deserts and sandy beaches.

God looked at the land with its rich, dark soil. He looked at the seas, shining and blue. God was happy.

God spoke again. "I want to make plants," he said. And plants appeared: tall plants, green plants, plants with seeds to make new plants, flowers and trees and grasses, plants on the land and plants in the water.

God looked around at what he had made. He had made the land and the sea and filled them with plants. He was very, very happy. "This is very good," he said.

Talk to God

Thank you, God, for the beautiful world. My favourite bit is...

Use the picture

1 You can use the picture as an introduction to the Bible story or to help you review the story together. Show the children the picture and encourage them to describe what they can see. Read the heading aloud: 'God makes land, sea and plants', pointing to the words as you do so. Can the children find the 'land' in the picture? And the 'sea and plants'?

2 Give the children the picture to decorate. They could colour, paint or use collage materials to fill the picture with bright and shiny effects.

3 Look at, and admire, the picture you have made. It is good! Tell the children that God looked at what he had made and said, 'That is good.' Thank God for making such a wonderful world!

God makes land, sea and plants Genesis 1:9–13

God makes stars and planets

Read it from the Bible

Genesis 1:14–19

'God said, "I command lights to appear in the sky and to separate day from night and to show the time for seasons, special days, and years. I command them to shine on the earth." And that's what happened.' *Genesis 1:14,15*

Tell the story

God made us a wonderful sky. In the daytime, it is bright and light blue and has a big shiny sun in it.

God made the sun to keep us warm and to light up the daytime.

God made us a wonderful sky. In the night-time, it is a dark deep blue and has a bright moon shining in it. Sometimes the moon looks big and round. Sometimes it is a shiny curve. And God made lots of stars to twinkle in the dark and to light up the night-time.

God loves us so much that he made beautiful stars and planets, the moon and the sun.

Talk to God

Thank you, God, for the sun that keeps us warm. Thank you for the beautiful moon and the twinkly stars that shine at night.

Use the picture

1 You can use the picture as an introduction to the Bible story or to help you review the story together. Show the children the picture and encourage them to describe what they can see. Read the heading aloud: 'God makes stars and planets', pointing to the words as you do so. Can the children find the stars and planets in the picture? Could one of them be the moon?

2 Give the children the picture to decorate. They could colour, paint or use collage materials to fill the picture with bright and shiny effects.

3 Look at, and admire, the picture you have made. It is good! Tell the children that God looked at what he had made and said, 'That is good.' Thank God for making such a wonderful world!

God makes stars and planets Genesis 1:14-19

A new place to live for Abram

Read it from the Bible

Genesis 13

"'I will give you and your family all the land you can see. It will be theirs for ever!'" *Genesis 13:15*

Tell the story

Abram and Sarai began their long journey. Abram was a very rich man and had lots of silver and gold. He also had lots of cows, sheep and goats. There were so many things to take.

Abram, Sarai and their servants travelled through the desert and stayed in many different places. They lived in tents. Wherever he was, Abram always remembered God. He was sure God would keep his promise.

One day, God said to Abram, "Look around you. I will give you all the land you can see. One day you will have a very big family – so big that you won't be able to count everyone. This land will always belong to you and your family."

Abram found a lovely place near some trees and put up the tents.

"Thank you, God, for keeping your promise," he said. "Thank you for our new place to live."

Talk to God

Thank you, God, that you always look after us and give us the things that we need.

Use the picture

1 You can use the picture as an introduction to the Bible story or to help you review the story together.

2 Do the children remember what God had told Abram to do? God had told him to leave his home. So Abram did. God said he would give Abram a new place to live and a large family. Has God done that?

3 Look at the picture of Abram and Lot with all their sheep. The sheep need water to drink and grass to eat. Let the children colour or decorate the picture with collage materials.

A new place to live for Abram Genesis 13

God's promise to Abram

Read it from the Bible

Genesis 15:1–6

'Then the LORD took Abram outside and said, "Look at the sky and see if you can count the stars. That's how many descendants you will have."' *Genesis 15:5*

Tell the story

One night, Abram was sitting inside his tent. He thought about all the things God had given him. I have a wife, Sarai. I have lots of animals, tents to live in, food to eat and God has given me this land to be my home.

Abram was still sad. I have no children, he thought. Who will share all the good things God has given me?

But God spoke to him. "Abram, you will have a son. Your family will become very big."

Abram was surprised. "I am too old to have children," he thought.

God took Abram outside. He looked up and saw hundreds and thousands of twinkling stars.

"Can you count the stars?" God asked him.

"There are too many," Abram said.

"There will be too many people to count in your family," said God.

Abram remembered that God always keeps his promises. He knew God would do what he said.

Talk to God

Thank you, God, that you kept your promises to Abram. Thank you that you keep your promises to us too.

Use the picture

1 You can use the picture as an introduction to the Bible story or to help you review the story together.

2 Do the children remember the story of Abram? God told him to leave his home. So Abram did. God said he would give Abram a new place to live. So God did. God said he would give Abram a large family. Has God done that?

3 Look at the picture of Abram. What is he looking at? Why is he doing that? God had told Abram he would have a large family. Now God said that Abram would have as many people in his family as there are stars in the sky! Is that a large family?!

4 Try counting how many people would be in the family, as you decorate the pictures. Add adhesive or glitter stars for extra sparkle. Emphasise that Abram knew God would do everything he said.

God's promise to Abram

Genesis 15:1–6

Abram's new name

Read it from the Bible

Genesis 17

"'I promise you that you will be the father of many nations. That's why I now change your name from Abram to Abraham.'" *Genesis 17: 4,5*

Tell the story

God said to Abram, "I want you to trust me and always obey me."

"I will," Abram replied.

Then God reminded him of the promises he had made to Abram and Sarai. "I promised you a new land to live in and a big family one day. Remember, I will give you a baby son."

"You always do what you say," replied Abram.

God told him, "I'm going to give you something else. I'm going to give you a new name."

Abram was surprised.

"A new name with a special meaning. I will call you Abraham, because your family will be very big one day. And Sarai's new name is Sarah which means 'princess' because she has a special place in my plans."

Abraham was pleased with their new names.

"And your son will be called 'Isaac'," God told him. "Abraham, Sarah and Isaac... I know your names and I want you to be close to me forever."

Talk to God

Thank you, God, that you know everything about us.

Use the picture

1 You can use the picture as an introduction to the Bible story or to help you review the story together.

2 Do the children remember the story of Abram? God told him to leave his home. So Abram did. God said he would give Abram a new place to live. So God did. God said he would give Abram a large family. Has God done that? Not yet.

3 Give the children the Bible-story picture. While they decorate the scene, say that God spoke to Abram and made his promise to Abram again. God would give Abram a large family. Abram knew that God would do what he said.

4 Can the children see Abram in their picture? Can they see Sarai? (The third person is another member of their household. The children could choose either man to be Abram.) Now God did something else. He gave Abram and Sarai special *new* names: Abraham and Sarah.

Abram's new name Genesis 17

Jacob's family

Read it from the Bible

Genesis 29:1–35

'Jacob worked seven years for Laban, but the time seemed like only a few days, because he loved Rachel so much.' *Genesis 29:20*

Tell the story

Jacob stayed at his Uncle Laban's house. He worked on his Uncle Laban's farm. Jacob married a woman called Leah. Then he married one called Rachel. They had lots of children. Jacob was very happy. He worked hard and soon he had lots of sheep and goats and camels.

Talk to God

Thank you, God, that you look after us wherever we go. Thank you too for the people who look after us.

Use the picture

1 Use this activity after the children have heard the Bible story. Look carefully at the enlarged picture together. Can the children identify the different people in it? As they do so, write that person's name on the paper.

2 Ask the children to look at the picture again, as you point to and name everyone in it. Cover the page and encourage the children to try to remember as many of the people in the picture as they can. Praise them for the amount of people they remember. Check to see if any people were missed.

3 Remind the children that Jacob was on his own when he went to live in a new place but, while he was there, he married and had children. God was with him in his new place.

4 Give each child a copy of the picture to keep as a reminder of the story.

Jacob's family Genesis 29:1–35

God blesses Jacob

Read it from the Bible

Genesis 35:1–15

'After God had gone, Jacob set up a large rock, so that he would remember what had happened there. Then he poured wine and olive oil on the rock to show that it was dedicated to God, and he named the place Bethel.' *Genesis 35:13–15*

Tell the story

Jacob had been on a difficult journey. Now he was home again and was friends with his brother Esau once more. God wanted to make Jacob happy.

God said to Jacob, "I am God and this is what I will do... Now your name is Jacob, but I will give you a new name. Your name will be Israel. You will have many children and grandchildren. Some of your family will even be kings. I will give you lots of land. It will belong to you and your family for ever."

God gave all these things to Jacob. God made Jacob happy.

Jacob wanted to remember the very special things God had done. So, he put a large rock on the ground to remember what God had done. He always remembered how God had made him happy.

Talk to God

Thank you, God, for all the special things you do for us. Help us to remember them when we think about you.

Use the picture

1 Use this picture as a reminder that God was with Jacob all the time as you review Jacob's story. Can the children remember any stories about Jacob? (Jacob and Esau, Jacob and Rachel, etc.) Remind them that God had been with Jacob in all these Bible stories.

2 Ask the children to put on aprons and provide a selection of paints, crayons and collage materials. Encourage the children to decorate the picture of Jacob.

3 Display and look at the finished pictures and ask the children how Jacob looks. He is happy because God has looked after him and been with him always. Remind the group that God also wants to be with each of them always.

God blesses Jacob Genesis 35:1–15

Joseph helps his family

Read it from the Bible

Genesis 42:1–13

'Since Joseph was governor of Egypt and in charge of selling grain, his brothers came to him and bowed with their faces to the ground. They did not recognize Joseph, but straight away he knew who they were ...' *Genesis 42:6–8*

Tell the story

Joseph's brothers were very hungry. Their tummies kept rumbling. They had no corn left to make into bread. Then their father had an idea.

"Here's some money," he said. "I've heard you can still buy corn in Egypt."

The brothers went to see the important man who looked after the barns. "Please sell us some of your corn," they said. "We are all very, very hungry."

Talk to God

Thank you, God, for looking after us when things go well and we are happy.

Use the picture

1 Do this activity after hearing the Bible story. Do the children remember the first part of the story of Joseph? (Being sold by his brothers as a slave. Going to Egypt. Finding favour with the pharaoh.) Look together at the picture and find Joseph. Notice that he is wearing different clothes from his brothers. Why? Help them to remember that Joseph was an important man in Egypt and his brothers were just visiting Egypt to buy food.

2 Point to Joseph. Say, 'Things were going well for Joseph. He had a good job, plenty to eat and wear. Did he need God to look after him?' Affirm that he did. God always looks after us when things are good, as well as when they are bad.

3 The children can glue wool (to represent hair) on Joseph and his brothers and colour or collage them. As they finish each character, encourage them to say, 'God was looking after him.'

Joseph helps his family Genesis 42:1–13

All together now!

Read it from the Bible

Genesis 45:1–13

'Since Joseph could no longer control his feelings in front of his servants, he sent them out of the room. When he was alone with his brothers, he told them, "I am Joseph." Then he cried so loudly that the Egyptians heard him and told about it in the king's palace.' *Genesis 45:1,2*

Tell the story

"Don't you remember me?" the man asked. "I'm your brother, Joseph. How's Dad?" The brothers were frightened because they had been so unkind to Joseph. But Joseph was really pleased to see his family again.

"It's all right," he told them. "I'm sure God planned this to happen so that I could look after you all. Come and live in Egypt with me. There's lots of food to eat here."

That's what they did. God had helped Joseph to help his family.

Talk to God

Thank you, God, that you are still looking after us, even when we are naughty and when we think everything has gone wrong.

Use the picture

1 You could do this activity before the Bible story. Can the children remember the story of Joseph? Look together at the picture and work out who the characters are. Joseph is dressed differently and the others are all his family, including his brothers. Why do the children think they all look happy?

2 As the children work on their pictures, see what they can remember of Joseph's story so far, mentioning some of the things that went wrong – Joseph's brothers hating him, making him go to Egypt, and so on. But all the time God was looking after Joseph – and his family.

3 Look at the picture together. Say that in today's Bible story they will find out what God had been planning for Joseph's family. They will soon know how God was going to help them and why they all looked so happy!

All together now! Genesis 45:1–13

Miriam

Read it from the Bible
Exodus 15:19–21 (and Exodus 2:1–10)

'The LORD covered the royal Egyptian cavalry and chariots with the sea, after the Israelites had walked safely through on dry ground.' *Exodus 15:19*

Tell the story

Miriam's family were friends of God. Her brothers Aaron and Moses became leaders of God's people. Miriam helped them and God gave her special messages for them.

But all God's people in Egypt were sad and frightened. The king of Egypt was very cruel to them. They tried to escape but the king's army followed them and chased them all the way to the sea. Moses said: "Don't worry, God will take care of us." And he was right.

God made a path through the sea so that they could walk across safely. When the king of Egypt's army arrived, God sent the water tumbling back. Moses and God's people were safe and free.

Miriam was so happy she began to sing and dance. She played her tambourine as she thanked God for keeping them safe. All the women followed her. Everyone praised God.

Talk to God

Thank you, God, that in the past you did amazing things to keep your people safe. Thank you that you keep us safe too!

Use the picture

1 You can use the picture as an introduction to the Bible story or to help you review the story together.

2 Show the children the picture of Miriam. Does she look happy or sad? What do they think she is doing? Tell them she is dancing and praising God because he has kept her people safe.

3 Can they decorate the picture to make it as bright and colourful and happy as possible?

4 Read the story again and encourage the children to make Miriam dance as she praises God for all he has done.

Miriam Exodus 15:19–21 (and Exodus 2:1–10)

27

A place to worship God

Read it from the Bible
Exodus 35:20 – 36:7; 39:32 – 40:38
'Men and women came willingly and gave all kinds of gold jewellery such as pins, earrings, rings and necklaces.' *Exodus 35:22*

Tell the story
God said, "Moses, I want my people to make a special tent where they can come to worship me. Ask the people for everything you need and I will show you what to do."

So Moses asked the people, "Come and bring gifts to make a special place to worship God. Bring your rings and bracelets; give your gold, silver and bronze metals. Give your best red, blue and purple wool; your wood and leather and finest cloth. Bring shiny stones, sweet spices and the best oils and perfumes."

The people brought all these gifts – and more!

God said, "Bezalel is very clever. He will make the special tent."

So Moses gave everything the people had brought to Bezalel. And Bezalel did what God told him to do. He made a beautiful place to worship God.

Talk to God
Dear God, thank you that you give us good things. Please help us to do our best for you too.

Use the picture
1 You can use the picture as an introduction to the Bible story or to help you review the story together.

2 Explain that Moses wanted to make a special place where people could go to worship God; to talk to him and sing about how wonderful he is. They are not going to make a building, because they keep moving from place to place. All the people are living in tents, so they are going to make a tent to worship God in too.

3 Look at the Bible-story picture. What can the children see? What have people given for the tent? Read a list of some of the things God asked them to give: gold, silver, shiny metal; red, blue and purple wool; the best cloth; leather; wood; sweet-smelling oil; sweet-smelling spices and shiny stones. Can the children see any of these in the picture?

4 Say that the people were happy to give their very best things to God because they wanted his special tent to be the very best it could be. Encourage the children to make their pictures the very best they can!

A place to worship God Exodus 35:20 – 36:7; 39:32 – 40:38

Joshua makes plans

Read it from the Bible

Joshua 2

'Joshua chose two men as spies and sent them from their camp at Acacia with these instructions:
"Go across the river and find out as much as you can about the whole region, especially about the town of Jericho."' *Joshua 2:1*

Tell the story

Joshua told the people, "We are going into the new land that God has promised. When you see the priests carrying God's special box, it will be time to go."

"How will we get across the river?" the people asked. "It's so deep and wide!"

Joshua said, "Our God, the God who made the whole earth, will help us. When the priests step into the water, the river will stop flowing and we'll all get across safely."

Talk to God

Thank you, God, that you have good plans for us.

Use the picture

1 You can use the picture as an introduction to the Bible story or to help you review the story together.

2 Point to the figure of Joshua and explain that Joshua is the leader of God's people. God has said that Joshua will lead the people to a new land. In this picture, Joshua is looking at the new land and thinking about what to do. Complete the picture of Joshua, by sticking on balls of tightly screwed-up paper. Make a pile of balls of paper first; then spread glue on one area of the picture at a time. Press the paper firmly into place.

3 The new land is across a river. Joshua and the people will need to cross the river to get to the new place to live. Use the same technique and complete the river.

4 Joshua decides to send some men to look at the new land and let him know what it is like. Colour the land on the far side of the river.

5 Is the picture finished now? Good! Now Joshua is ready to go...!

God chooses Gideon

Read it from the Bible

Judges 6:11–16,33–40

'Gideon replied, "But how can I rescue Israel? My clan is the weakest one in Manasseh, and everyone else in my family is more important than I am."' *Judges 6:15*

Tell the story

Bash, bash, bash! Gideon was knocking the corn-grains from the stalks. And Gideon was not happy. "I grew this corn. I want to make it into bread. But if those Midianite soldiers find me, they'll take it away. And I'll have no bread." Gideon wished a strong, brave hero would chase the Midianite soldiers away.

Gideon looked up. An angel was sitting looking at him! "Hello, Strong Brave Hero," the angel said. "God has chosen you."

Gideon gasped, "Not me! I'm not strong or brave."

The angel told him, "God has chosen you to chase the Midianites away."

Gideon shook his head. "I'm very weak, though. All my family are weak. And I'm the weakest of all."

The angel said, "You can chase the Midianites away if God helps you." Gideon began to understand. He would learn to be strong and brave. God had chosen him.

Talk to God

Thank you, God, that you know us really well. You know us even better than the grown-ups who look after us.

Use the picture

1 You can use the picture as an introduction to the Bible story or to help you review the story together.

2 Look at the picture and see that one of the characters shown is a messenger from God. The messenger is talking to Gideon and is saying that Gideon is a strong, brave leader.

3 Does Gideon look very brave? No – and he did not think he was, either! But the messenger has come from God. It is not the messenger who thinks Gideon is strong and brave – it is God!

4 Complete the picture, making God's messenger bright and shiny.

5 Do the children think Gideon will be brave and strong? God says he is!

Gideon listens to God

Read it from the Bible

Judges 7:1–22

'The LORD said, "Gideon, your army is too big. I can't let you win with this many soldiers. The Israelites would think that they had won the battle all by themselves and that I didn't have anything to do with it."' *Judges 7:2*

Tell the story

"My army is very big," thought Gideon. "We'll easily chase the Midianites away."

God said, "Your army is too big, Gideon. They'll win easily. They will forget that I helped them." Gideon listened to God. He sent some of his soldiers home. God said, "The army is still too big. Send more away."

Gideon listened to God. He sent away more soldiers. "Now," Gideon thought, "my army is small."

"It's just the right size," God told him. "Now I'll help you chase the Midianites away."

Gideon's army went out at night. Each soldier had a trumpet and a fiery torch hidden in a clay jar. They crept around the Midianite army. Gideon blew his trumpet! Everyone smashed their clay jars. The torches blazed with light. They blew their trumpets. The Midianites were scared. They ran away! God had helped Gideon, and Gideon had learned to listen to God.

Talk to God

Thank you, God, that Gideon became a great leader, just as you promised.

Use the picture

1 You can use the picture as an introduction to the Bible story or to help you review the story together.

2 Show the picture of Gideon's soldiers. Gideon and his men are going to fight another army who want to hurt God's people. Gideon does not have many men in his army. The enemy army has got lots and lots of soldiers. But God is helping Gideon – and God has told Gideon what to do. Who do the children think will win?

3 Look at the soldiers. See that each man has a pot (on the ground) and is holding a trumpet in one hand and a light (a fire-torch) in the other hand.

4 Guide the children to colour the elements of the picture as you mention them. 'This is what God has told them to do. First they all break their pots. Bang, bang, bang.' Wait while the children colour the pots. 'Then everyone will see their lights, bright and shining in the dark night.' Decorate the lights. 'And then Gideon's men will blow their trumpets. Toot, toot, TOOT!' Colour the trumpets and the men.

5 Can the children guess what happened? The other army was confused and the men were frightened. Gideon's men did not need to fight at all. God won for them!

Gideon listens to God _{Judges 7:1–22}

35

Samson

Read it from the Bible

Judges 13:1–7; 16:4–31

'... one day an angel from the LORD appeared to her and said: "You have never been able to have any children, but very soon you will be pregnant and have a son. He will belong to God from the day he is born, so his hair must never be cut ..."'

Judges 13:3–5

Tell the story

Everyone wondered why Samson was strong – so strong that he could fight God's enemies – and win every time! Only Samson, his mother and father knew why.

"Why are you so strong?" asked Delilah. (She had promised to find out and tell God's enemies so they could stop Samson winning all the fights.)

Samson teased her: "Tie me up with seven new ropes. I won't be strong then." But Samson was quite strong enough to break the ropes.

"You lied to me," Delilah cried. "Please tell me why you are so strong."

Then Samson told the truth. "God makes me strong," he said. "I've never had my hair cut, to show I belong to God."

In the night, Delilah cut his hair. When Samson woke up his strength had gone. God's enemies caught him and made him a prisoner.

But Samson's hair grew. God made him strong again – strong enough to fight for God!

Talk to God

God, you are amazing. You know what we will be like before we are born.

Use the picture

1 You can use the picture as an introduction to the Bible story or to help you review the story together.

2 Give the children the Samson picture. Encourage them to describe him. Does he look strong or weak? Is his hair long or short?

3 Let the children complete their pictures. Help them tape his long hair in place. (Sticky tape is easier than glue, for this.)

4 If your child is willing, you could demonstrate cutting off Samson's hair! (But take care: the artwork may be very precious to your child!) Tape fresh strands in place as his hair grows again.

Samson Judges 13:1–7; 16:4–31

37

Naomi and Ruth

Read it from the Bible

Ruth 1

"'I will go where you go,
I will live where you live;
your people will be my people,
your God will be my God ...'" *Ruth 1:16*

Tell the story

Naomi was an old woman. Her husband and two sons
had died while the family were living in another country.
Now, Naomi wanted to go back home to Bethlehem.

Her sons had married two girls called Orpah and Ruth.
They both began to go with Naomi on her journey.
They loved Naomi very much and wanted to look after
her. "No," said Naomi, "this isn't fair. You shouldn't be
looking after me. I'm an old woman now. You should go
back to Moab where your own families live. You are still
young. Perhaps God will give you both new husbands
and some children."

Orpah and Ruth cried. They loved Naomi very much.
They did not want to leave her. Orpah decided to go
back home to Moab, but Ruth said to Naomi, "I want
to live where you live. I want to worship your God. I will
never leave you."

Talk to God

Thank you, God, that Ruth and Naomi cared for each
other. Thank you that you loved them too!

Use the picture

1 You can use the picture as an
introduction to the Bible story
or to help you review the story
together.

2 Compare the two women in
the picture. Work out which is
Naomi (the older woman) and
which is Ruth (the younger one).
Glue scraps of fabric to their
clothes, to give texture.

3 Comment that a lot of sad
things have happened to Naomi
and Ruth. But Naomi and Ruth
love each other – and they both
love God. God loves them and is
looking after them.

Naomi and
Ruth

Ruth 1

Ruth and Boaz

Read it from the Bible

Ruth 2–4

'... Ruth went out to pick up grain in a field owned by Boaz. He was a relative of Naomi's husband Elimelech, as well as a rich and important man.' *Ruth 2:3*

Tell the story

Every day, Ruth went to pick up the left-over grains of corn from a farmer's field. Then she took the corn home and ground it into flour to make bread for her and Naomi to eat.

Boaz, the farmer, was a rich and important man. He saw Ruth working hard. "Who is that woman picking up corn from my field?" Boaz asked his workers.

"She lives with Naomi," they said. The farmer knew Naomi because she was part of his family. Boaz was very kind.

"Look after Ruth and always leave extra corn for her," he told his men. "And let her drink from my water jars whenever she is thirsty."

Boaz liked Ruth so much that he married her. When they had a baby boy, Naomi was really pleased to become a grandma. She knew God had looked after her and Ruth in a wonderful way.

Talk to God

Thank you, God, that you made Ruth and Naomi happy.

Use the picture

1 You can use the picture as an introduction to the Bible story or to help you review the story together.

2 Look at the Bible-story picture from the previous page, if you used it, and compare it with the picture on this page. Where is Naomi in the new picture? Where is Ruth? But what has happened? Who else is in the picture?

3 If the children have not yet heard the full Bible story, introduce the man as Boaz: he loves Ruth and they are married. They will have a baby called Obed: Ruth and Boaz will be his mummy and daddy. Naomi will have a family and she will be happy.

4 Ruth, Boaz and Naomi know that God loves them. When they were sad, he looked after them. And now he has made them all happy together!

Ruth and Boaz Ruth 2–4

41

King for ever

Read it from the Bible

2 Samuel 7

"'I will make sure that one of your descendants will always be king.'" *2 Samuel 7:16*

Tell the story

King David loved God. One day God sent Nathan to King David, with a message.

"King David," said Nathan, "God has told me to say this to you. 'David, I have helped you and I have made you the king of this land. You are going to be a good king. And I promise that someone from your family will always be king.'"

David listened to everything that Nathan said. Then David talked to God: "God, this is so wonderful! Thank you for telling me about it. You are so great! And you do such great things for us! Thank you that someone from my family will always be king."

David was happy because God has said he would do so many good things. And David knew that God would do what he said he would do.

Talk to God

Thank you, God, that you always keep your promises.

Use the picture

1 You can use the picture as an introduction to the Bible story or to help you review the story together.

2 Turn the picture into a 'commemorative poster' to mark the grand occasion of David being king!

3 Decorate the border of the picture with bright patterns (use gold and silver if available). Complete the picture in bright, happy colours.

4 Hold up the poster and say, 'God promised David that someone from his family would always be king. Hurray for King David! Hurray for God!' All repeat, 'Hurray for King David! Hurray for God!'

King for ever

2 Samuel 7

Mephibosheth

Read it from the Bible

2 Samuel 9

'Mephibosheth was lame, but he lived in Jerusalem and ate at David's table, just like one of David's own sons...' *2 Samuel 9:11–13*

Tell the story

King David was thinking. He looked around. "What a lot of lovely things I have, now that I am the king," he said. "I have a big palace with lots of rooms. I have the best food and drink. I have a beautiful bed and all the clothes I want! God has been very kind to me. I have everything I want."

King David said, "I would like to be kind to someone as God has been so kind to me. Who needs help?"

David's servant Ziba suggested, "There is a young man from your friend Jonathan's family. He is called Mephibosheth. But he can't walk very well. There is something wrong with his feet."

"Please bring him to me," said David.

So Ziba brought Mephibosheth to meet David. David was pleased to see him.

"I want to be kind to you," David said. "I will give you a room in my palace, a place to sleep and clothes to wear. I want you to come and eat your meals with me, every day."

"Thank you, King David," smiled Mephibosheth. "You are very kind to me."

Talk to God

Dear God, help us to be kind to other people.

Use the picture

1 You can use the picture as an introduction to the Bible story or to help you review the story together.

2 Show how kind David was to Mephibosheth by adding more details to the picture. Fill any spaces with food, clothes, and anything else that he might need.

3 Why do the children think David was so kind?

Mephibosheth 2 Samuel 9

God speaks to Elijah

Read it from the Bible

1 Kings 19:1–18

'"Go out and stand on the mountain," the LORD replied. "I want you to see me when I pass by."...' *1 Kings 19:11*

Tell the story

Queen Jezebel was angry. She wanted to hurt Elijah. So he ran away and hid in a cave on a mountain. "What are you doing here?" God asked.

"I'm unhappy," Elijah replied. "I've always tried my best to obey you, but other people don't want to worship you like I do. Some of them even want to hurt me."

"Go outside the cave," God told Elijah. "Stand on the mountain. I want you to see that I'm here with you." Elijah waited. Suddenly, there was a strong wind. Rocks began to move. But Elijah did not see God. Then the ground began to shake. But Elijah did not see God.

Elijah felt a gentle breeze blowing all around him. He covered his face with his cloak. Elijah knew God was with him. He was sure God understood why he was unhappy.

Then Elijah listened as God promised to help him.

Talk to God

Thank you, God, that you know all about us. There is nowhere we can hide from you!

Use the picture

1 You can use the picture as an introduction to the Bible story or to help you review the story together. You will need to wrap a puppet or teddy and 'hide' it in a box before you begin.

2 Say that you have brought a toy – but it is hiding somewhere. Ask the the children to help you find it. When they have guessed the box, open it slowly and bring out the wrapped puppet or teddy. Say that the toy is still hiding: perhaps the children could ask it to come out to play? As they do so, remove the blanket and show them the hidden toy.

3 Say that this reminds you of a Bible story. Elijah (the children may remember him from other sessions) hid from the king and queen who wanted to hurt him. He did not hide in a box! He hid in a cave – but God knew he was there and God called him to come out and talk with him.

4 See Elijah standing at the entrance to the cave in the picture. He is still afraid and he is hiding behind his coat! But God talks to him and Elijah does not need to hide any more.

God speaks to Elijah 1 Kings 19:1–18

47

Elisha helps a poor family

Read it from the Bible

2 Kings 4:1–7

'Elisha told her, "Ask your neighbours for their empty jars. And after you've borrowed as many as you can, go home and shut the door behind you and your sons. Then begin filling the jars with oil and set each one aside as you fill it."' *2 Kings 4:3,4*

Tell the story

"Elisha!" called a voice. Elisha turned around.

There was a poor woman with her two boys.

"Please help us, Elisha," she said. "We have no food and no money. My sons are hungry."

"What do you have at home?" Elisha asked.

"Only a little olive oil in a jar," she said.

Elisha knew that God would help them, so he said, "Ask your neighbours for lots of empty jars. Then do what I tell you."

The woman and her two boys began to knock on all the neighbours' doors. They soon had lots and lots of jars. Next, Elisha told the woman to go indoors and take their jar of oil and pour it into the other jars.

She filled up one jar, then another and another and another.

"Wow!" said the boys. "All that oil from one little jar!"

"Elisha knew God would help us," she said. "Now we can sell the oil and buy some food."

Talk to God

Thank you, God, that you can do amazing things!

Use the picture

1 You can use the picture as an introduction to the Bible story or to help you review the story together.

2 Look at the Bible-story picture and count how many people you can see. Explain that these people are a family: a mum and her two sons.

3 See if the children can count the pots and jars in the picture: how many are there? The pots were empty but now the mum is pouring something into them: what could it be? Explain that the tiny jar in her hand has oil in it – and she is going to fill all those big jars with oil from just that little jar. Act puzzled about this: how could it happen? There are lots of big jars and not much oil in that one little jar.

4 Say that one person is missing from the picture. One of God's messengers, Elisha, told the woman what to do. And Elisha knew because God told him. Find out what happened with today's Bible story.

Elisha helps a poor family 2 Kings 4:1–7

A home for Elisha

Read it from the Bible

2 Kings 4:8–37

'... "I'm sure the man who comes here so often is a prophet of God. Why don't we build him a small room on the flat roof of our house? We can put a bed, a table and chair, and an oil lamp in it. Then whenever he comes, he can stay with us."'

2 Kings 4:9,10

Tell the story

Elisha was visiting a town called Shunem.

A woman asked, "Would you like to have a meal with us?"

"Thank you," said Elisha. He was hungry and he had a long way to walk home. He enjoyed his meal with the woman and her husband.

"Eat with us every time you come to Shunem," they said.

One day, when Elisha came to Shunem, the woman was waiting outside her house as usual, but the house looked different. There was a new room on the roof! "Come and look," she said.

She took him up the stairs and opened the door. Inside there was a bed, a table, a stool and a lamp.

"It is all for you, Elisha," the woman said. "We know how hard you work for God. You can stay here whenever you come to Shunem."

"Thank you," said Elisha. "Now I don't have to walk all the way home every night."

Talk to God

Dear God, please show us how to do kind things to help other people.

Use the picture

1 You can use the picture as an introduction to the Bible story or to help you review the story together.

2 Look around you: can you see the walls that make a room? A chair? A light? Somewhere to sleep?

3 Now look at the Bible-story picture. Can the children find a room? Somewhere to sit and sleep?

4 See the three people just outside this room. They are a husband and wife standing together. The other man is called Elisha. Do the children know what is happening in this scene?

5 Either read today's Bible story to explain or say that these kind people have built this special room, just for Elisha. It is their way of helping him do his work for God. He will have somewhere warm and comfortable to stay, when he is going from place to place.

A home for Elisha 2 Kings 4:8–37

Elisha and Naaman

Read it from the Bible

2 Kings 5:1–19

'Elisha sent someone outside to say to him,
"Go and wash seven times in the River Jordan.
Then you'll be completely cured."' *2 Kings 5:10*

Tell the story

Naaman's skin was covered with nasty sores that hurt
and itched! He heard that a man in Israel could make him
well. It was Elisha, who worked for God. Naaman took his
servants and lots of presents and went to Israel.

Naaman found Elisha's house and knocked on the door.
Elisha's servant answered.

"Elisha says to go and wash yourself seven times in the
river," the servant told Naaman. "Then God will make
you well."

"I'm a very important man!" shouted Naaman. "I want to
see Elisha himself!"

The servant shut the door. Naaman was angry, but his
servants said, "Go and wash in the river. It's not hard to
do and God will make you well."

Naaman went to the river. He washed himself once,
twice, three times, four, five, six times. When he had
washed seven times, all his spots and sores had gone.
God had made him well again.

Talk to God

Thank you, God, that you can make poorly people well
again. Please can you make ... well again.

Use the picture

1 You can use the picture as an
introduction to the Bible story
or to help you review the story
together.

2 Show the children the picture.
Tell the children that Naaman,
the man in the river, was not
very well. His skin was sore and
there was nothing the doctors
could do to make him well
again.

3 If possible, make a copy of
the picture to do this activity.
Let the children paint Naaman,
using thin watercolour paints, to
show how poorly he was.

4 Say that God made Naaman
better. Elisha told Naaman to
wash seven times in the river.
Count slowly from one to seven.

5 On 'seven', brush over the
painted Naamans with clean
water, so the paint is diluted and
fades away. See how God made
Naaman well again, when
Naaman did as Elisha said.

Elisha and Naaman 2 Kings 5:1–19

God talks to Elisha

Read it from the Bible

2 Kings 6:8–23

'"Don't be afraid," Elisha answered. "There are more troops on our side than on theirs." Then he prayed, "Lord, please help him to see." And the LORD let the servant see that the hill was covered with fiery horses and flaming chariots all around Elisha.' 2 Kings 6:16,17

Tell the story

Elisha was in danger. Soldiers were coming to find and capture him.

One day, Elisha's servant came out of Elisha's house. He saw lots of soldiers with horses and chariots everywhere. He ran back inside to tell Elisha. "What shall we do?" the servant cried. "There are so many soldiers and only two of us. They'll get us for sure."

"No," said Elisha. "There are more soldiers fighting on our side." Then Elisha prayed, "Let my servant see." And when the servant looked again, he could see God's army with fiery chariots ready to look after Elisha!

When the soldiers started to attack, Elisha prayed again: "Stop the soldiers from seeing me." And God answered his prayer. The soldiers could not see! Elisha went up to them. "You're in the wrong place," he told them. And he took them to the king who gave them a great feast and sent them home again!

God had kept Elisha safe. And Elisha went on working for God.

Talk to God

Thank you, God, that you look after us and keep us safe.

Use the picture

1 You can use the picture as an introduction to the Bible story or to help you review the story together.

2 Let the children begin colouring with ordinary crayons or colouring pencils.

3 Tell the story and say that Elisha was not afraid because he knew that God's army was keeping him safe.

4 Provide as many exciting and exotic collage materials as you can, so the children can make God's army dazzle! Encourage them to draw in extra members of God's army in these dazzling colours.

God talks to Elisha 2 Kings 6:8-23

Hezekiah trusts God

Read it from the Bible

2 Kings 18:13 – 19:37

'"I promise that the king of Assyria won't get into Jerusalem, or shoot an arrow into the city, or even surround it and prepare to attack. As surely as I am the LORD, he will return by the way he came and will never enter Jerusalem."'

2 Kings 19:32,33

Tell the story

There was a huge enemy army outside the walls of the city. King Hezekiah and his people were inside.

One of the leaders of the enemy army shouted, "You can't stop us! God won't help you! We will take over your city!"

Hezekiah talked to God. "The army is very big and very strong. Please help us," he asked.

God sent his messenger Isaiah to talk to the king. "We can trust God," Isaiah explained. "God says that the army will not hurt us. God will protect us and the city."

Hezekiah believed God's message. He trusted God.

And the next morning, the whole enemy army had gone!

Talk to God

Thank you, God, that we can trust you, just like Hezekiah did.

Use the picture

1 You can use the picture as an introduction to the Bible story or to help you review the story together.

2 Show the children the Bible-story picture and ask them which person looks like a king. Point to him and say, 'This is King Hezekiah.' Introduce the other person as Isaiah: he is one of God's messengers.

3 Explain that the picture shows Isaiah telling Hezekiah what God says. Say, 'I wonder what he said?' and then tell the Bible story to find out more about the story.

Hezekiah trusts God 2 Kings 18:13 – 19:37

Hezekiah and Isaiah

Read it from the Bible

2 Kings 20:1–11

'"… I heard you pray and I saw you cry. I will heal you, so that three days from now you will be able to worship in my temple."' *2 Kings 20:5*

Tell the story

King Hezekiah was very ill. He talked to God. "I have always tried to do what you wanted," King Hezekiah said, crying because he was so sad and he felt so poorly.

God sent his messenger Isaiah to talk to the king. "God has heard you," Isaiah explained. "He will make you well again. In three days' time you will be well enough to walk around. You will even be able to go to worship God in the Temple." Then Isaiah told the servants what to do to make Hezekiah better.

And three days later, Hezekiah was better! He was so well that he could go to worship God in the Temple. God had kept his promise.

Talk to God

It's good to say thank you to you, God, for all the good things you do.

Use the picture

1 You can use the picture as an introduction to the Bible story or to help you review the story together.

2 Ask the children what they can see in the Bible-story picture. Identify King Hezekiah: they may remember him from last time, if you used the previous spread. Do they know what the building is? It's the Temple, a place where people went to sing and talk with God. That's why Hezekiah is going there: he wants to thank God for something.

3 Listen to the Bible story to find out what Hezekiah wanted to say 'thank you' for.

Hezekiah and Isaiah 2 Kings 20:1–11

Josiah becomes king

Read it from the Bible

2 Kings 22:1–13; 23:1–3

'When Josiah heard what was in The Book of God's Law, he tore his clothes in sorrow.'

2 Kings 22:11

Tell the story

King Josiah was a good king.

He taught the people to worship and pray to God.

King Josiah decided that the Temple, the building where people went to worship God, needed cleaning and mending. People swept and dusted and polished. They sawed and hammered. Then someone found an old book.

In the book were God's words and all the things that God wanted his people to do! What an important book!

When King Josiah read the book, he was very sad. The people had not been doing what God's words said they should. So Josiah called everyone together. He read the book to them so that everyone would know what God wanted them to do.

Talk to God

Thank you, God, for the Bible. Thank you too for all the people who help us learn about you from the Bible.

Use the picture

1 You can use the picture as an introduction to the Bible story or to help you review the story together.

2 Ask the children which person looks like a king in the Bible-story picture. The man wearing the crown is King Josiah. Chat about what he is doing, what he is reading and how he is feeling: does he look happy, sad, surprised, worried or something else?

3 Say that when Josiah read the words on the scroll, he found out that he had not been living God's way and nor had the people in his kingdom. What do the children think Josiah will do?

4 Explain that Josiah was a good king and he wanted everyone to do what God said. He read the words to all the people so everyone could begin to live God's way.

Josiah becomes king 2 Kings 22:1–13; 23:1–3

Josiah reads God's book

Read it from the Bible

2 Kings 23:1–23

'After Josiah had finished reading, he stood by one of the columns. He asked the people to promise in the LORD's name to obey the LORD faithfully and to follow his commands. The people agreed to do everything written in the book.' *2 Kings 23:3*

Tell the story

King Josiah read God's words. He was sad because he knew that he and the people had not been doing what God wanted. Josiah asked God to forgive him.

But Josiah was also glad because now he knew what God wanted him to do. Josiah gathered all the people together and made a promise to God. Josiah said,

"I promise you, Lord God, that I will obey you. I will do the things that are written in the Bible."

Josiah knew that God's words are for everyone, so he asked all the people to promise to obey God's words.

Josiah kept his promise! He celebrated and praised God, just as it said in the Bible. All the people joined in, playing music, eating together and having a wonderful time worshipping God.

King Josiah did everything just as God's word said.

Talk to God

Thank you, God, for the Bible. Thank you too for all the people who help us to learn about you from the Bible.

Use the picture

1 You can use the picture as an introduction to the Bible story or to help you review the story together.

2 See if the children remember good King Josiah from last time, if you looked at the previous spread. Find him again on today's Bible-story picture. He is still holding the scroll of the words from God – but what is he doing now? And what are all the other people doing, too?

3 Explain that King Josiah told everyone what God said and how they could all live God's way. They all wanted to thank God – and that's what they are doing in the picture.

4 Complete the picture using bright, happy colours to celebrate.

Josiah reads God's book 2 Kings 23:1–23

Ezra

Read it from the Bible

Ezra 7; Nehemiah 8:1–10

'The people started crying when God's Law was read to them. Then Nehemiah the governor, Ezra the priest and teacher, and the Levites who had been teaching the people all said, "This is a special day for the LORD, and he will make you happy and strong."' *Nehemiah 8:9*

Tell the story

When Ezra came to Jerusalem, he shook his head sadly. The people who lived in the city had no one to teach them what God wanted. They were doing things which were wrong, but they would not listen to Ezra.

One day, Ezra had a visitor. The man said. "We want to know God and do what is right."

Ezra jumped up, took the Book of the Law carefully and followed the man. Everyone was waiting. He began to read the book, telling them what God wanted.

He said, "God wants you to meet him and know him. Listen to what he wants."

The people said, "We will!"

"Then have a party," Ezra told them. "Today is a happy day!"

Talk to God

Dear God, thank you for all the people who help us to know you better.

Use the picture

1 You can use the picture as an introduction to the Bible story or to help you review the story together.

2 Look at the Bible-story picture and ask the children to say which character they think is Ezra. Ask, 'Who are the other people?' and 'What is Ezra doing?' Establish that Ezra is helping the people to know God. When people play sports they need a coach – someone to help them know what to do better. Ezra was their coach, helping them to know God better.

3 Encourage the children to colour Ezra and then the rest of the picture. As they work, ask, 'Who tells you about God?' Help them see that when they hear Bible stories or when they say prayers or talk about him, someone is helping them know God.

Nehemiah builds

Read it from the Bible

Nehemiah 1,2,4

'..."Those captives who have come back are having all kinds of troubles. They are terribly disgraced, Jerusalem's walls are broken down, and its gates have been burnt."' *Nehemiah 1:3*

Tell the story

Hello, I'm Nehemiah. When I got home to Jerusalem, I looked all around the city at night. Just as my brother had told me, the walls were all broken down and the gates had been burnt.

I would need a lot of help to rebuild the walls and make Jerusalem safe from our enemies. But would the people be willing to help?

In the morning, I called the people of Jerusalem together. I said, "Jerusalem is in a real mess. The walls are broken down and the gates are burnt. We must build the walls and gates again so we can be proud of our city. Our enemies will try to stop us, but God has been good to us. He will keep his promise to look after us. The king will send us the wood we need. Will you help?"

The people all stood up and said, "Let's start today!"

And the work began.

Talk to God

Thank you, God, for people who listen to you. Help us to be like that too.

Use the picture

1 You can use the picture as an introduction to the Bible story or to help you review the story together.

2 Describe how important it was, in Bible times, for a city to have a strong wall all around it, to keep everyone safe. Say that you are going to hear about the city of Jerusalem. Can any of the children spot anything wrong with the strong walls on the picture? (They are falling down.) Will they be much good for keeping the people and the city safe now?

3 Say that someone is going to put things right. His name is Nehemiah and he has come from a country far away to make sure the walls of Jerusalem are built again. Find Nehemiah in the picture and see that other people are going to help him build the walls.

4 Do the children think the walls will be built again?

5 Colour the picture. You could cut out and stick on some stones to help Nehemiah rebuild the walls.

Nehemiah builds Nehemiah 1,2,4

Nehemiah celebrates

Read it from the Bible
Nehemiah 12:27–43, Psalm 126

'God had made the people very happy, and so on that day they celebrated and offered many sacrifices. The women and the children joined in the festivities, and joyful shouts could be heard far from the city of Jerusalem.' *Nehemiah 12:43*

Tell the story

Hello, I'm Nehemiah! What a celebration we had when we'd finished building the walls around Jerusalem. We were safe from our enemies and God had helped us. This is what we did.

We had singing and music with people clashing cymbals and playing harps – all to praise God for helping us. We climbed up onto the top of the wide, wide wall and marched around, one group walking one way around the wall and another group walking the other way.

Then we stopped outside the Temple and praised God again, this time with trumpets and loud singing. God had made us very happy and so we sang with all our hearts and worshipped him.

Then the people said, "We will live as God wants us to. We will keep his rules."

All the men, women and children joined in. They shouted so happily that the sound could be heard from far away!

Talk to God

Thank you, God, that you helped Nehemiah to rebuild the walls of Jerusalem.

Use the picture

1 You can use the picture as an introduction to the Bible story or to help you review the story together.

2 Say that the walls of Jerusalem were falling down. You could show the children the picture from the previous page to remind them. Nehemiah and the people worked so hard that, soon, the walls were built again.

3 See how tall and strong the walls look now in the picture. Point to Nehemiah and the people: how are they feeling after all their hard work?

4 Explain that Nehemiah knew God had helped them. What do the children think happened next? The people walked all round the walls shouting and singing their thanks to God.

5 You could cut out and stick bright coloured stones on the walls in the picture, and collage or colour the people's celebration.

Nehemiah celebrates Nehemiah 12:27-43, Psalm 126

Beautiful Esther

Read it from the Bible

Esther 1–4

"'Bring together all the Jews in Susa and tell them to go without eating for my sake! Don't eat or drink for three days and nights. My servant girls and I will do the same. Then I will go in to see the king, even if it means I must die.'" *Esther 4:16*

Tell the story

King Xerxes needed a new wife. He brought all the most beautiful girls in the country to his palace. One of them was Esther. She was a Jew, one of God's special people.

All the girls were well looked after. They had special treatment to make them more beautiful. Then the king chose one to be his wife. It was Esther.

She did not tell the king she was a Jew.

One day, Esther's cousin Mordecai told her that all the Jews were in danger. Their enemy Haman was trying to get rid of them all.

Mordecai told her, "The king believed Haman's lies. All the Jews will be killed."

Esther was upset. She knew that she had to help. "Although I am the queen," she said, "I cannot go to the king just when I like. But I will go and see if I can change his mind. Tell all the Jews to pray for me."

Talk to God

Thank you, God, for making Esther brave. Help us to be brave too when we are scared.

Use the picture

1 You can use the picture as an introduction to the Bible story or to help you review the story together.

2 Look at the story picture and comment that Esther was very beautiful – the king (sitting in the background) married her because she was the most beautiful girl in the kingdom.

3 Before the children start work on their pictures, suggest they think about how they can make Esther look lovely. What colours will they use?

4 Who else is in the picture? The man talking to Esther is her cousin, a man called Mordecai. He is asking Esther to do something very brave. Do the children think she will do it?

Esther saves God's people

Read it from the Bible

Esther 5–10

'Esther answered, "Your Majesty, if you really care for me and are willing to help, you can save me and my people. That's what I really want, because a reward has been promised to anyone who kills my people ..."' *Esther 7:3,4*

Tell the story

Esther knew that God's people were in danger. Haman was telling lies that made the king hate God's people, the Jews. They would all be hurt unless she went to the king and told him the truth.

But, although she was the queen, she could not go to the king whenever she wanted. She had to wait for him to ask her to come.

What could she do? She thought of a clever plan.

Bravely, she went to the king. He was not angry, so she said, "Come to a party I'm having. It's just for you and Haman."

The king was very pleased. At the party, he told Esther she could have anything she wanted.

"Then please save my people, the Jews," she said. "Our enemy Haman wants to get rid of us."

The king was angry with Haman. "I will stop Haman hurting your people," he said. And he sent Haman away. Esther had saved God's people.

Talk to God

Thank you, God, that you kept your people safe from their enemies.

Use the picture

1 You can use the picture as an introduction to the Bible story or to help you review the story together.

2 Identify the three people in the Bible-story picture. One is Esther: she is a woman and she is very beautiful. Which one is she? Can the children colour or decorate her to make her look even more beautiful? Esther is married to King Xerxes: he wears a crown and sits on a special chair to show he is important. Which one is he? Can they decorate or colour him to look important? The other person is called Haman. Can the children remember who he is from the story?

Esther saves God's people Esther 5–10

God keeps me safe

Read it from the Bible

Psalm 25

'Show me your paths
and teach me to follow;
guide me by your truth
and instruct me.
You keep me safe,
And I always trust you.' *Psalm 25:4,5*

Tell the story

The shepherd knew the sheep were thirsty. He needed to take them to water. He called: "Come on, time for a drink!" At once the sheep ran towards him. They trusted him to look after them.

The shepherd led the way. Well, thought the shepherd, that reminds me of the song I'm making up. He began to sing:

"I bring my prayers to you, O Lord,
Because I trust in you."

But as he walked along, one of the sheep wandered off down the wrong path. "Come back!" called the shepherd. "There's no water that way. You might get lost or hurt." And the shepherd thought; that reminds me of my song too. So he sang:

"When I go wrong, O Lord God,
You teach me the right way.
You lead me because I want to follow you.
You keep me safe!"

Happily singing his song to God, the shepherd took the sheep to water.

Talk to God

Thank you, God, that you look after us and keep us safe.

Use the picture

1 You can use the picture as an introduction to the Bible story or to help you review the story together.

2 Print colours on the picture, by dipping a cotton wool ball into paint and then pressing it on the paper. Work from the top of the page and make a blue sky. Then change to green and use a fresh cotton wool ball to make grass for the sheep to eat.

3 Let the paint dry before printing the sheep itself.

4 Why do the children think the sheep looks so happy? It knows the farmer (shepherd) cares for it and will keep it safe. God loves and cares for us too: he wants us to be safe always.

God keeps me safe Psalm 25

Wonderful God

Read it from the Bible

Psalm 95:1–7

'He holds the deepest part
of the earth in his hands,
and the mountain peaks
belong to him.' *Psalm 95:4*

Tell the story

This world has always been beautiful. When God created
it, long, long ago it was big, wonderful, amazing and
awesome. God made it for his people to live in.

So, when people saw how good the world was, they
wanted to thank God. So they said: "Come on, everyone,
let's sing a song of joy to God."

They saw the deep valleys and said, "God, you made the
deepest valleys and you are great!"

They saw the steep hills and mountains and said, "God,
you made the highest mountains and you are great!"

They saw the sea and all the creatures living in it and
said, "God, you made the sea and you are great!"

They saw the dry land and the plants, animals and
people that live on it and said, "God you made the dry
land and you are great! We are your people and you
care for us!"

Talk to God

God, you made all our wonderful world – that's just
amazing! Thank you.

Use the picture

1 You can use the picture as an
introduction to the Bible story
or to help you review the story
together.

2 Encourage the children to use
all their creativity to decorate
the picture. You could add glitter
to the water, cotton wool to the
snowy mountain tops, sequins
on the fish, tissue paper flowers
and trees – anything to make
God's world look amazing.

3 When the picture is finished,
say these words from Psalm 95:
God 'rules over the whole earth,
from the deepest caves to the
highest hills. He rules over the
sea, which he made; the land
also, which he himself formed.'
(Good News Bible)

4 Give God a good clap!

Wonderful God Psalm 95:1–7

God cares for me

Read it from the Bible

Psalm 103:1–5

'Each day that we live,
he provides for our needs
and gives us the strength
of a young eagle.' *Psalm 103:5*

Tell the story

I am going to praise God
I am going to say how
   great he is.
God is great.

I am going to praise God.
I remember how kind
   he is.
God is kind.

I am going to praise God.
God forgives us when we
   do wrong.
God forgives.

I am going to praise God.
He makes us well when
   we are sick.
God heals us.

I am going to praise God.
He keeps us safe from
   harm.
God keeps us safe.

I am going to praise God.
He gives us his love.
God loves us.

I am going to praise God.
He gives us everything we
   need.
God gives.

I am going to praise God.
He makes us strong, as
   strong as eagles!
God makes us strong.
Praise God!

Use the picture

1 You can use the picture as an introduction to the Bible story or to help you review the story together.

2 Tell the children about one of the songs in the Bible (Psalm 103:5) where it says that God 'gives us the strength of a young eagle'. Be excited by this image and enthuse to the children!

3 Decorate your own pictures of a strong young eagle. This activity will be easier if you are able to copy the page. Set out trays of paint and give each child a feather. Show them how to lay the feather gently on the paint and then press it on their picture, to give the eagle some feathers. This is going to be messy so supervise the activity closely, and be ready to wash painty hands as soon as each child has finished.

4 Talk with the children about how strong and beautiful their eagle looks. Look at the picture together and say the psalm verse again.

Talk to God

Thank you, God, for all the wonderful ways that you look after us.

God cares for me Psalm 103:1–5

God's love goes on and on and on

Read it from the Bible

Psalm 136:1–9

'Praise the LORD! He is good.
God's love never fails.' *Psalm 136:1*

Tell the story

In the Bible, take a look,
    wonderful words in God's own book.
Praise the Lord! He is good!
    His love goes on and on and on.
Amazing things are what he does.
    His love goes on and on and on.
His people know how strong he is.
    His love goes on and on and on.
There's no one quite as strong as God.
    His love goes on and on and on.
He made the sky above our heads.
    His love goes on and on and on.
He stretched the land across the sea.
    His love goes on and on and on.
He made the bright lights in the sky.
    His love goes on and on and on.
He made the sun to rule each day.
    His love goes on and on and on.
The moon and stars to rule each night.
    His love goes on and on and on.
In the Bible, take a look,
    wonderful words
    in God's own book.

Talk to God

God, your love goes on and on and on and on – for ever.
Thank you.

Use the picture

1 You can use the picture as an introduction to the Bible story or to help you review the story together.

2 Give the children a variety of materials to make the story picture into a collage. Show them how to put the glue on the picture first and then stick the collage pieces and scraps in place.

3 As you add each collage scrap you could repeat the words, 'God's love goes on and on'. Or you could use the words once each element of the picture is completed.

God's love goes on and on and on and on Psalm 136:1–9

God loves me!

Read it from the Bible

Psalm 139

'You are the one who put me together
inside my mother's body,
and I praise you
because of the wonderful way
you created me...' *Psalm 139:13,14*

Tell the story

When I stand and walk upstairs,
God knows and he cares.
When I go out or just stay at home,
God knows and he cares.
When I go to play with my friends,
God knows and he cares.
If I get up to see the sun rise,
God knows and he cares.
If I'm up late and the dark scares,
God knows and he cares.
Before I was born, God knew I was there,
God knows and he cares.
As I get bigger, God watches me still,
God knows and he cares.
Wherever I go, whatever I do,
God knows and he cares.

Talk to God

Dear God, you know all about us. You even knew about
us before we were born. Thank you.

Use the picture

1 You can use the picture as an introduction to the Bible story or to help you review the story together.

2 Look at the picture of the baby and read Psalm 139:16: '... with your own eyes you saw my body being formed. Even before I was born, you had written in your book everything I would do.' Wow! God knows everything about us: now, when we were babies, even before we were babies!

3 Compare the baby with yourselves. What does the baby look like? Has he/she got hands, legs, eyes, a body? How does a baby eat, move, speak? And how about you? As you colour, marvel at the way you have grown and changed – and yet all started as babies.

God loves me! Psalm 139

God is with us

Read it from the Bible

Psalm 145

'Each generation will announce
to the next your wonderful
and powerful deeds.' *Psalm 145:4*

Tell the story

God is with us.
You're my king and you are great.
I will thank you for ever and ever.
Every day I'm going to thank you.
I will praise you for ever and ever.
Mums and dads, grandparents too,
They all want to sing praise to you.
They'll tell all the good things you've done,
How you're good and kind and great,
And you love us every day.
Dogs, cats, birds and people too,
Sing their praise and love to you.
You're our king for ever and ever,
And you'll always keep your promise.
You help us when we're in trouble,
And pick us up when we fall down.
You give us food and all good things.
Yes! We know you're king of kings!
You care for us and keep us safe.
We love you, Lord, and praise your name.
We love you, Lord, and praise your name.

Talk to God

God, you are with us always. Thank you.

Use the picture

1 You can use the picture as an introduction to the Bible story or to help you review the story together.

2 List all the times the children sing songs or hear music: perhaps they sing at nursery or school, at home, watching the TV, at a church group.

3 Look at the Bible-story picture together. Ask the children, 'What are these people doing?' Work out that they are singing – but why? Let the children come up with ideas and guide them, gently, to the idea that these people are singing to God.

4 You could play or sing along to praise songs, while the children complete their pictures.

God is with us Psalm 145

Jeremiah sees a potter

Read it from the Bible

Jeremiah 18:1–12

'The LORD told me, "Go to the pottery shop, and when you get there, I will tell you what to say to the people."' *Jeremiah 18:1,2*

Tell the story

God told Jeremiah to go down to the pottery shop. The shop did not just sell pottery. Jeremiah could go and watch the potter making pots and jars and bowls from clay.

The potter shaped the clay with his wet hands. He pulled the clay with his fingers and thumbs, making the shape taller, smoother and rounder or sometimes – whoops! – wobbly and wonky! When that happened, or if the potter did not like the shape of the pot he had made, he squashed the clay together and started again. The potter wanted his pots to be the very best he could make. He worked and worked until each and every pot was perfect.

God told Jeremiah to tell the people that he wanted them to be the very best people they could be. And God would work and work to make them his perfect people, just like the potter worked to make his pots perfect.

Talk to God

Dear God, thank you that you are kind to us when we say sorry to you for the naughty things we've done.

Use the picture

1 You can use the picture as an introduction to the Bible story or to help you review the story together.

2 Ask the children to describe what they can see on the Bible-story picture. What do they think the man sitting down is doing? (Making pots.) Use the words 'potter' and 'pottery' to help the children develop their understanding.

3 Introduce the other person in the picture as Jeremiah, one of God's friends and messengers. Say that God told Jeremiah to go and watch the potter making his pots.

Jeremiah sees a potter Jeremiah 18:1–12

Jeremiah buys a field

Read it from the Bible

Jeremiah 31:1–6; 32:1–15

'Hanamel came, just as the LORD had promised. And he said, "Please buy my field near Anathoth in the territory of the Benjamin tribe. You have the right to buy it, and if you do, it will stay in our family."

'The LORD had told me to buy it from Hanamel, and so I did ...' *Jeremiah 32:8,9*

Tell the story

God told Jeremiah to buy a field. But Jeremiah was in prison! How could he buy a field? And how could he look after it? How could he grow plants or have farm animals to eat the grass?

Jeremiah's cousin came to see him. "I have a field to sell," he said. "Would you like to buy it?"

"This must be the field God wants me to buy," Jeremiah realised. Jeremiah paid his cousin some money. His cousin gave Jeremiah a piece of paper that said the field now belonged to Jeremiah. Jeremiah put the paper away safely. He still did not know how he was going to look after his new field.

Then God said to him, "One day, all my people will be free to look after their fields again."

Jeremiah did not know when that day would be – but he knew that God always does what he says he will.

Talk to God

Dear God, thank you that you kept your promise to Jeremiah. Thank you that you keep your promises to us too.

Use the picture

1 You can use the picture as an introduction to the Bible story or to help you review the story together.

2 On the blank piece of paper, ask the children to imagine they have a field and draw what they would do with it. They may cover it with green grass, keep cows, grow plants, play – anything they like.

3 Now look at the picture of Jeremiah with the field he bought. When he bought it, he knew he could not keep cows or grow flowers or play in it (list the things the children have drawn in their fields), maybe for a long time. But he knew that, one day, he would be able to – because God had told him so, and he knew he could trust what God said.

Jeremiah buys a field Jeremiah 31:1–6; 32:1–15

Jeremiah and the scroll

Read it from the Bible

Jeremiah 36

'I had told Baruch what to write on that first scroll, but King Jehoiakim had burnt it. So the LORD told me to get another scroll and write down everything that had been on the first one.'

Jeremiah 36:27,28

Tell the story

Jeremiah was God's messenger. He told the people what God told him. But the people did not want to listen. They told Jeremiah to stop.

Jeremiah kept speaking God's words. His helper, Baruch, wrote the words on a scroll. Baruch read the words aloud to the people. The people did not want to listen. They took the scroll to the king! "Read!" ordered the king.

One man opened the scroll. "God wants you to obey him," he read.

"I don't want to listen to this!" growled the king. He cut a piece off the scroll and threw it into the fire. Each time the man read a few words, the king cut them up and burned them – until the whole scroll was gone!

God spoke to Jeremiah again. Jeremiah told Baruch what to write. And Baruch wrote it all down again on another scroll. The king could not stop God's words!

Talk to God

Dear God, thank you that you want to talk to us. Help us to listen to you.

Use the picture

1 You can use the picture as an introduction to the Bible story or to help you review the story together.

2 Point to the figure of Jeremiah on the Bible-story picture. The children may remember him if you looked at the previous pages. Remind them, if necessary, that Jeremiah is one of God's friends and messengers. In this Bible story, God has given Jeremiah a message to give to the people. Jeremiah is saying what God has said; and Baruch is busy writing all the words down.

3 When the children have completed their story-pictures, suggest they take a blank sheet of paper and cover it with 'writing' (real words or squiggly patterns are fine).

4 Show them how to roll up the paper from both ends to make a scroll.

Jeremiah and the scroll Jeremiah 36

Jeremiah down the well

Read it from the Bible

Jeremiah 38:1–13

'So the four of them went to the king and said, "You should put Jeremiah to death, because he is making the soldiers and everyone else lose hope. He isn't trying to help our people; he's trying to harm them."' *Jeremiah 38:4*

Tell the story

Some men wanted to get Jeremiah into trouble. The king said they could punish Jeremiah. They put him into a deep, dark hole. The sides were steep and slippery. There was gooey mud at the bottom of the deep hole. Jeremiah could not get out.

But a good man, who worked for the king, heard about what had happened. He went to see the king. "Your Majesty," he said, "this is not fair. Jeremiah has done nothing wrong. If Jeremiah stays down that hole, he will have nothing to eat and he will die."

The king listened to what the good man said. "All right," he agreed. "Get Jeremiah out."

The good man found some ropes, took some men to help him and, together, they pulled and pulled till Jeremiah was out of the muddy hole.

Jeremiah still had a job to do. He was still God's messenger.

Talk to God

Thank you, God, for people who do good things and help other people.

Use the picture

1 You can use the picture as an introduction to the Bible story or to help you review the story together.

2 Look at the Bible-story picture and sound relieved as you do so: Jeremiah was down a well but – good – now some kind men are pulling him to safety.

3 Make sure that the children know what a 'well' is; then ask: 'Did Jeremiah fall down the well?' (No!) 'Did Jeremiah want to be down the well?' (No!) 'Did someone put him down the well?' (Yes!) But who would do that? Find out in the Bible story or review it together.

Jeremiah down the well Jeremiah 38:1–13

Shadrach, Meshach and Abednego

Read it from the Bible

Daniel 3

'"But I see four men walking around in the fire," the king replied. "None of them is tied up or harmed, and the fourth one looks like a god."'

Daniel 3:25

Tell the story

The king built a huge golden statue and ordered all the important people in the country to stand in front of it. "When you hear the music playing," he told them, "you must bow down and worship the statue."

The music played, the trumpets, flutes and harps. Everyone bowed down to worship the golden statue – everyone except Daniel's three friends. "We will only worship God," they said. "He will look after us."

The king was very angry. "I'll give you another chance," he shouted. "When you hear the music playing, bow down and worship the statue or I'll throw you into the fire."

The music played, the trumpets, flutes and harps. But the three friends did not bow down.

The king had them thrown into the fire. To his surprise the friends were not hurt at all!

The king got the friends out of the fire. "God looked after you," he said. "Now everyone must worship your God."

Talk to God

Thank you, God, for the amazing way you looked after Shadrach, Meshach and Abednego.

Use the picture

1 You can use the picture as an introduction to the Bible story or to help you review the story together.

2 Look at the picture of Shadrach, Meshach and Abednego and let the children decide who is who (there is no right or wrong answer). Describe the events briefly: the king made a statue and told everyone to bow down to worship it; these men did not.

3 Ask the children how many men are not bowing down. Why do they think these three are not bowing down? Establish that the three men will not worship anyone or anything except God.

4 Let the children colour in the three friends who are standing up for God. If the children have not noticed yet, point out the flame shapes in the background. Say that God protected the men from the fire. (But be sure to point out that fire is very hot and could hurt them, so they should definitely not try this themselves!) Colour the flames or cover them in small pieces of colourful or shiny paper.

Shadrach, Meshach and Abednego Daniel 3

First steps in Bible reading
The *Tiddlywinks* range of Little Books

My Little Red Book
First steps in Bible reading
Reese discovers Christmas is coming...
978 1 85999 659 1

My Little Yellow Book
First steps in Bible reading
Danny finds out about Easter.
978 1 85999 693 5

My Little Blue Book
First steps in Bible reading
Lucy and Liam find out about me...
978 1 85999 660 7

My Little Green Book
First steps in Bible reading
Krista explores God's wonderful world
978 1 85999 696 6

My Little Purple Book
First steps in Bible reading
Lily discovers 'Jesus loves me'.
978 1 85999 720 8

My Little Orange Book
First steps in Bible reading
Jamie looks inside God's book.
978 1 85999 717 8

Tiddlywinks Little Books are designed to be used at home by a parent/carer with an individual child. Linked to the themes covered in the *Tiddlywinks* Big Books, children can discover and learn about the Bible and share their discoveries with you. There are 50 first steps in Bible reading pages in each book, with a story for each day and extra activity pages of fun things to do. Children will love exploring the Bible with child characters Lucy and Liam, Reese, Danny, Krista, Lily and Jamie.
A5, 64pp £3.50 each (Prices subject to change)

You can order these or any other *Tiddlywinks* resources from:
● Your local Christian bookstore
● Scripture Union Mail Order: Telephone 01908 856006
● Online: log on to **www.scriptureunion.org.uk/tiddlywinks** to order securely from our online bookshop

66 When the Big Books are used in conjunction with the Little Books children and adults encounter an attractive mixture of stories and activities that will encourage everybody to know and trust in Jesus. 99
Diana Turner,
Editor of Playleader Magazine

The flexible resource for pre-school children and carers

Also now on sale
Say and Sing. Glitter and Glue. Make and De...